Cover illustration: A Panzerbefehlswagen III Ausf H command vehicle awaits the order to move out. This vehicle was a modification of the standard gun tank, major differences including a dummy gun, a turret bolted in place, and the addition of a number of observation and pistol ports; three variations of this vehicle appeared throughout the war, differing only in the radios carried. This example belongs to a member of the regimental command staff, as indicated by the letter 'R' on the turret side plate. The harshness of the desert night is indicated by the long-sleeved tunics and overcoats worn by the crew.

1. Elements of a DAK unit race across the desert: a PzKpfw 1 Ausf B leads a pair of staff cars and an SdKfz 254 Beobachtungspanzer. Only 128 SdKfz 254s were produced, and the vehicle is known to have served with the 15th Panzer Division in North Africa.

Afrika Korps

GEORGE BALIN

ARMS AND ARMOUR PRESS

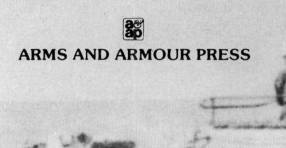

Introduction

ublished in 1985 by Arms and Armour Press
-6 Hampstead High Street, London NW3 1QQ.

Distributed in the United States by
terling Publishing Co. Inc., 2 Park Avenue,
New York, N.Y. 10016.

British Library Cataloguing in Publication Data:
Balin, George
Afrika Korps. – (Tanks illustrated; no. 17)
. Germany. *Heer. Afrikakorps*
. Tanks (Military science) – Pictorial works
. Title   II. Series
23.74'752'0943   UG446.5
SBN 0-85388-692-0

Editing, design and artwork by Roger Chesneau.
Typesetting by Typesetters (Birmingham) Ltd.
Printed and bound in Italy.
y Tipolitografia G. Canale & C. S.p.A. - Turin
n association with Keats European Ltd.

*This book is dedicated to Cary, Julie, Maria, and my
fellow employees at Leyden Customs Expediters Inc.*

Generalfeldmarschal Erwin Rommel – the 'Desert Fox', as he
has come to be known amongst historians – has long been a
popular subject in military history. Since the end of the Second
World War, and in fact even while the conflict was taking
place, the 'Desert Fox' was a name held in high esteem by
friend and foe alike. In addition, the various armoured vehicles
that were used by the Deutsches Afrika Korps have attracted a
lot of interest from military vehicle enthusiasts and plastic
modellers alike.

Rommel's role in the North African Campaign began on
6 February 1941 and lasted until he was recalled to Berlin on
9 March 1943. Throughout this period he proved his great
ability and leadership time and time again. Even though
usually outnumbered in both men and equipment he was able
to win an impressive chain of victories from Libya to Tunisia,
but ultimately even the genius of the 'Desert Fox' was out-
matched by the numerical superiority of the Allies.

The bulk of the material for this volume was gleaned from
the photograph files of the US National Archives in
Washington, DC. The extensive collection at the National
Archives includes a large number of captured German wartime
photographs and also a recently declassified set of photos
linked to Rommel himself, although it is unclear whether this
collection represents photographs taken by the 'Desert Fox'
himself or photographs presented to him. Throughout this
volume the reader will see also photographs illustrating DAK
vehicles during all phases of the campaign, from the initial
unloading in Tripoli in February 1941, through the fighting in
the Western Desert, to the last days in Tunisia in May 1943.
The author has tried to provide views of all the major vehicles
used by the DAK, as well as by their Italian allies; in addition,
photographs of captured British and US types in German
service are included.

George J. Balin

◀2
2. Generalleutnant Erwin Rommel in his SdKfz 250/3
Leichter Funkpanzerwagen. 'Greif', used by
Rommel during his drive on Tobruk in 1942, was
painted in panzer grey with a sand overspray,
although here the original grey finish is beginning to
show through in several places.

▲3

3. A PzKpfw 1 Ausf A (SdKfz 101) being unloaded in Tripoli in late February 1941. The vehicle still retains the panzer grey paint scheme used in Europe; in addition it carries the numeral 'I', indicating that it is the battalion command tank for the 1st Battalion, as well as insignia indicating a vehicle originally belonging to the 3rd Panzer Division.

4. A PzKpfw 1 Ausf A on the quayside in Tripoli, February 1941. The vehicle was part of the 5th Leichte (Light) Division, formed from elements of the 3rd Panzer Division. This photograph provides a good view of the rear of the vehicle, this area having the major differences that distinguished the Ausf A from the B (both of which appeared during the North African campaign).

▼4

5. A 5th Leichte Division Kleiner Panzerbefehlswagen 1 Ausf A (SdKfz 265) is offloaded in Tripoli in late February 1941. The vehicle is assigned to the Headquarters unit.

6. A PzKpfw II Ausf F moves down the road in Tripoli, late February 1941. The number '144' indicates 1st Company, 4th Platoon, 4th tank.

7. A PzKpfw III Ausf G or H being unloaded in Tripoli, February 1941. The vehicle belongs to the 1st Company, 3rd Platoon (but was formerly of the 3rd Panzer Division), and will shortly have a rough application of DAK yellow applied over its panzer grey finish.
8. A PzKpfw III Ausf G of the same unit is lowered on to the quayside.
9. A German column enters an unidentified town in Libya. The column consists primarily of soft-skinned vehicles, but is led by a

Leichter Panzerspähwagen (MG) SdKfz 221.
10. A German reconnaissance unit checks for signs of enemy activity near Gazala, April 1942. The vehicle illustrated is the Leichter Panzerspähwagen (MG) SdKfz 221 armoured car. The vehicle was light in weight, which gave it a good cross country performance, but its single 7.92mm MG34 armament meant that it was usually operated alongside the 2cm-armed SdKfz 222 armoured car.

▲11   ▼12

11. This photograph has been included to illustrate the use of tank turrets in fixed gun positions. Unfortunately, the location and exact date are not certain, but the photograph is interesting in that it shows a British Matilda Mk II cruiser tank turret, from a vehicle that was perhaps knocked out in the earlier fighting in the Western Desert.

12. Elements of Rommel's command group during a halt in the desert: Rommel's personal SdKfz 250/3, nicknamed 'Greif'; an SdKfz 251/6 Mittlerer Kommandopanzerwagen Ausf B; and an SdKfz 251 Mittlerer Schützenpanzerwagen Ausf C. The 251/1 Ausf C at the end carries a personal name on its nose, but it is unfortunately not clear enough to make out. The photograph was probably taken during Rommel's drive on Tobruk in June 1942.

13. On the move: the 'Desert Fox' advances in 'Greif' along with elements of a motorized column. This photograph is from a famous series showing the general sharing some recently liberated canned peaches with some of the crew of his command SdKfz 250/3. Several British soft-skinned trucks can be seen in the background, illustrating how captured vehicles were put to use whenever possible. A command version SdKfz 251/6 Mittlerer Kommandopanzerwagen passes on the right.

▲14

14. Rommel, in his command vehicle, awaits the results of some newly issued orders from his forward units; this view shows clearly how the command aerial was attached to the vehicle's hull. Note that the colour within the letters of the name 'Greif' appears to be lighter than the black of the Balkenkreuz, seeming to confirm that the colour used was red. On the right-hand side, the name appeared in white outline only.

15. Rommel awaits reports from point units.

16. Rommel and members of his command staff tour the front. The Wehrmacht serial number carried by Rommel's SdKfz 250/3 was WH-937836.

17. A Deutsches Afrika Korps command post. The vehicle in the background is a mobile command post on a truck chassis; that in the foreground is an SdKfz 251/6 Mittlerer Kommandopanzerwagen. The 251/6 was a fully equipped command vehicle which carried the FuG 11 and FuG Tr 100MW radio sets necessary to allow communication between a commander and his forward troops.

▼15

▲18

18. Another view of the wheeled mobile command post used by Rommel, in tow behind an SdKfz 251/6.

19. A poor quality but nonetheless interesting view showing the 9m mast fitted for the FuG 11 transmitter. The German designation for this vehicle was SdKfz 251/3 IV Mittlerer Funkpanzerwagen, a radio command vehicle used in controlling armoured formations. This particular variant carried both an FuG 11 and an FuG 12 radio transmitter.

▼19

20. A mobile command post using an AEC Armoured Command Vehicle captured from the British 2nd Armoured Division when the latter was overrun at Mekili in April 1941, one of three such vehicles taken and handed over to Rommel. Two were retained by Rommel for his personal use, but the third (illustrated) was handed over to General Streich. This particular vehicle originally bore the headquarters number '5' on the nose, hull sides, and rear, as well as the serial number L4426428, the 2nd Armoured Division insignia, the unit code box, and the number '12' within a circle. The photograph shows that the original paint scheme is intact, as well as most of the original markings, but the crew has taken the precaution to add German identity crosses, the one seen here obscuring the original HQ number.

21. A Leichter Panzerspähwagen (2cm) SdKfz 222 passing one of Rommel's AEC Armoured Command Vehicles; the latter is that believed to have been dubbed 'Max' at a later date.

▲22

22, 23. Two photographs depicting Rommel in one of his personal AEC ACVs; note that the name 'Max' or 'Moritz' has not yet been added. The original colour scheme has been modified by painting the nose of the vehicle in DAK yellow, together with some swirls of either blue or panzer grey (it is possible that some captured British paints may have been utilized). The sides of the vehicle still carry the British disruptive paint scheme, and no markings are visible except for a German cross on the nose and the HQ insignia on the right front wing. It is the author's opinion that this vehicle later became 'Max'.

24. 'Max' on the move in the North African hills; this particular AEC ACV is believed to have been given by Rommel to his operations staff. The vehicle still retains the original British disruptive paint scheme, but carries full German markings. The original British vehicle number '2' can be seen, together with part of the serial number, which is possibly L4426424. German markings consist of a national cross and two DAK insignia, one in white and the other in black.

25. Members of Rommel's command staff in front of one of the captured 'Mammut' command vehicles, probably 'Moritz'.

23▲   24▲ 25▼

▲26 ▼27

28▲ 29▼

26. Afrika Korps personnel gather around Rommel's 'Mammut' command vehicle; this vehicle was nicknamed 'Moritz' and became Rommel's favourite. It appears in its second paint scheme.
27. One of Rommel's 'Mammut' command vehicles and an SdKfz 251/6 Mittlerer Kommandopanzerwagen move off to the front.
28. Rommel's command group during a stop near the front lines. Note the unusual outlined Balkenkreuz on the SdKfz 251/6.
29. Members of a reconnaissance unit take a rest while waiting for further orders. The vehicle illustrated is the SdKfz 222 Leichter Panzerspähwagen (2cm) light armoured car, and markings indicate that it belonged to the 15th Panzer Division, probably Panzer Regiment 8 – it is believed that the *Totenkopf* (Death's Head) pennant was flown by that unit in Africa.

19

▲30 ▼31

0. Members of a Leichter Panzerspähwagen SdKfz 222 armoured car crew prepare to move out. The 2cm gun of this vehicle proved to be a very effective weapon in the wide expanses of the desert.
1. A Leichter Panzerspäh-wagen unit on a reconnaissance mission near the front.
2. Elements of a reconnaissance unit meet in the desert: an SdKfz 231 waits while a Leichter Panzerspähwagen (2cm) SdKfz 222 keeps an eye out for the main force to catch up.
3. Fuel was the 'life blood' of an army in the desert. Large numbers of fuel cans were carried, and captured ones were often pressed into service. Here two members of a Leichter Panzerspähwagen (2cm) SdKfz 22 fill their tank.

32▲   33▼

▲34

34. A light armoured car detachment receives orders to move out, and two officers check out a map before mounting up. The vehicles shown are a pair of Leichter Panzerspähwagen (2cm) SdKfz 222 armoured cars and a Leichter Panzerspähwagen (Fu) SdKfz 223.
35. Members of the crew of a Leichter Panzerspähwagen (Fu) SdKfz 223 push their vehicle out of a dune. The SdKfz 223 was a successful attempt to provide a light armoured car with a long-range radio set.

▼35

36. The crew of an SdKfz 231 armoured car clean the gun of their vehicle. Cleanliness was all-important in the desert as sand managed to get into everything!
37. A crew member of a Schwerer Panzerspähwagen SdKfz 231 8-Rad waves a Nazi flag to an approaching aircraft. In the vast expanses of the desert it often proved difficult for pilots to identify targets before attacking, and it was common for crews to drape large national flags over their vehicles to show their identity.

38. The crew of a Schwerer Panzerspähwagen (Fu) SdKfz 232 8-Rad scans the horizon for signs of enemy activity.

39. Members of the Afrika Korps make music as a Schwerer Panzerspähwagen (Fu) passes by on the way to the front. The main function of the SdKfz 232 8-Rad was to provide support to smaller units, which would usually be equipped with the lighter, four-wheeled armoured cars.

40. A front view of the same SdKfz 232 as that shown in the previous photograph. These vehicles served alongside SdKfz 231 heavy armoured cars within the heavy section of a Panzerspähwagen squadron of a motorized Aufklarungs detachment.

41. Elements of a command group meet up in the desert; the photograph shows an SdKfz 263 Panzerfunkwagen 8-Rad and a PzKpfw III Ausf F. The SdKfz 263 was a conversion of the SdKfz 231 armoured car, and was introduced in 1938 as a mobile base communications vehicle for command staff. Its single 7.92mm MG34 made it unsuitable as a fighting vehicle, and it usually operated alongside other armoured vehicles. Note the track sections applied to the hull of the tank for extra protection.

▲38 ▼39

42. The same pair of vehicles from another angle. Note that, owing to the limited space inside the SdKfz 263, the crew have had to attach most of their personal gear to the wings of their vehicle: tents, bags, packs, water cans, tools, firewood, etc. can be seen, all required to make the hardship of life in the desert more bearable.

43. Crew members of an SdKfz 263 Panzerfunkwagen 8-Rad converse during halt. The view clearly shows the method by which the radio mast was mounted to the turret. Armament consisted of a single 7.92mm MG34 machine gun, but there were also several pistol ports to enable the crew to fire from within the vehicle.

44. A Panzerfunkwagen SdKfz 263 8-Rad makes its way to the front. This vehicle carried a 1 Satz Funkgerät für (m) Pz Funktrupp b.

45. Elements of a DAK tank unit advancing across the open desert: in the foreground a PzKpfw 1 Ausf B, in the background a pair of 4.7cm Pak(t) (Sf) auf PzKpfw 1 Ausf B Panzerjägers.

▲42 ▼43

▲46   ▼47

46. Rommel and an unidentified staff officer examine a knocked-out British Rolls-Royce 1920-Pattern armoured car. This vehicle was abandoned during the fighting in the Western Desert, and probably belonged to the 11th Hussars.

47. General Rommel and some of his staff inspect a knocked-out British M3 Honey. The photograph dates from the period of Operation 'Crusader' in 1942.

48. Important victories were won by the DAK in the early days of the North African campaign. Here, a PzKpfw III Ausf G passes an abandoned British Matilda Mk. II cruiser tank in 1941. Note that scorching has burned some of the paint down to the original two-tone green scheme used before the vehicles were shipped to North Africa in 1940. The German tank has the divisional insignia for the 15th Panzer Division on the left front plate of the hull.

49. A German-crewed Matilda Mk. II tank awaits the order to move out. This tank was one of many captured types in German service; it carries German markings, and a flag for aerial identification is also prominent.

▲50 ▼51

52 ▲

50. Another captured Matilda Mk. II cruiser tank in service with the DAK. Note the remains of the British serial, as well as the German crosses on the front track guard and turret side.

51. Although poor in quality, this photograph is interesting because it shows a Stuart tank in German service. The vehicle may have been repainted in German DAK yellow, but the only marking visible is a German identification cross painted on the hull. Note the cover over the main gun, and the large amount of personal stores attached to the exterior of the vehicle.

52. A poor quality photograph of a German-marked CMP Chevrolet truck used as a portee for a 6pdr anti-tank gun.

53. Another former British vehicle impressed into service by the DAK, in this case a Morris Commercial Tractor, 4×4 Field Artillery, which was introduced in 1938–39 into the British Army. Note the two ammunition trailers, plus the 25pdr field piece in tow. The only marking evident is a German swastika in white on the door of the tractor.

53 ▼

▲54
54. A Panzerbefehlswagen III Ausf H pauses during a lull in the fighting. The photograph was taken in Libya in 1941; the vehicle belongs to an unidentified DAK unit.

55. A PzKpfw III Ausf J in Libya, 1941. The white-outlined red number '1' would seem to indicate a vehicle of the 1st Company, 8th Panzer Regiment, 15th Panzer Division.

▼55

56. A PzKpfw III Ausf G leads a column of armoured vehicles down a road in Cyrenaica (eastern Libya) in 1942; other vehicles visible include a Panzer I and a Panzer II. The PzKpfw III has the turret number 'R03', indicating the regimental signals officer.

57. Members of a command staff set up a temporary base camp during a lull in the fighting; the vehicle here is a PzKpfw III Ausf J armed with the 5cm Kwk L/42 tank gun, its command role indicated by the pennant flying from the radio antenna. Barely visible on the original print is the name 'Bestie', located immediately above the hull side vision port and apparently painted red or black. The photograph was taken in April 1942, approximately 45 miles west of Gazala.

58. A Panzerbefehls-wagen III Ausf H moves past a medical unit on its way to the front.
59. A PzKpfw III Ausf G waits to move out. Note the command pennant flying from the radio mast.
60. A PzKpfw III Ausf J passes a burning British soft-skin column. The crew of the tank have gone to great lengths to give additional protection to their vehicle: note the track links on the hull front and turret side.

60▼

▲61   ▼62

61. A Panzerbefehls-wagen III Ausf H or J heads a motorized column on the move. This command version of the Panzer III served with the headquarters sections of Panzer regiments. Note the captured CMP truck being used to transport supplies to the front.

62. A fine character study of a DAK tanker, who looks only a little the worse for running into some flying shrapnel. His vehicle is a PzKpfw IV Ausf E, armed with the 7.5cm Kwk 37 L/24.

63. Crew members of a 4.7cm Pak(t) (Sf) auf PzKpfw 1 Ausf B inspect a number of British prisoners. This vehicle matched a Skoda 4.7cm anti-tank gun and a PzKpfw 1 Ausf B chassis.

64. Members of an Italian reconnaissance unit wait for orders to move out. The vehicle in the background is a South African-produced Marmon-Herrington Mk. II captured during the fighting.

63▲ 64▼

37

▲65

65. Fiat-Ansaldo M13/40 2^A serie or 3^A serie medium tanks move up to the front. The crews have placed sandbags on the hull for added protection against anti-tank guns.

66. An Italian medium tank company in the North African desert. The vehicles illustrated are Fiat-Ansaldo M13/40 tanks either of the 2^A serie or 3^A serie (as indicated by the short track guards).

66 ▼

▲67   ▼68

67. An Italian Fiat-Ansaldo M13/40 medium tank makes its way to the front. The M13/40 2^A serie featured a square-shaped radiator collector, while the 3^A serie had a mushroom-shaped collector, but the fitting is unfortunately not visible from this angle. Note that the crew have stowed numerous fuel cans and much personal equipment on the outside of the vehicle; they have also added some scrub brush in an attempt to break up the outline of the vehicle. Some basic attempts at extra protection have been made – note the sandbags on the front of the hull.

68. Italian tankers pose with their Fiat-Ansaldo M13/40, the standard medium tank in the Italian Army throughout the war.

69. An Italian Carro Commando M40 command vehicle in the North African desert. The photograph was probably taken during the recapture of Cyrenaica in January 1942. These vehicles provided liaison between Semovente assault guns and their headquarters units, and were based on the M13/40 medium tank series.

70. Members of an Italian self-propelled assault gun unit advance across the desert. The photograph shows an M40 command vehicle in the lead, with a pair of Semovente DA75/18 M40 self-propelled assault guns following behind.

▲71 ▼72

71. Crew members of an Italian Semovente DA75/18 M40 self-propelled assault gun take a break during a lull in the fighting. The numeral '3' within the circle would seem to indicate a vehicle of the 3rd Battery.

72. Two 4.7cm Pak(t) (Sf) auf PzKpfw 1 Ausf Bs lead a truck convoy across the North African desert. This vehicle was among the first of many self-propelled guns built by the Germans during the war and using a foreign-made weapon – in this case the Czech 4.7cm anti-tank gun.

73▲ 74▼

73. A front view of a 15cm sIG 33 auf Fahrgestell PzKpfw II (Sf) self-propelled heavy infantry gun, of which only twelve examples were produced.

74. A Panzerjäger 38(t) für 7.62cm Pak 36(r) SdKfz 139 rolls onward. This vehicle was based on the Czech Panzer 38(t) and armed with a captured Russian 7.62cm anti-tank gun. The first six vehicles of this type made their way to North Africa in May 1942 and were attached to the Headquarters of the Tank Army in Africa.

▲75 ▼76

75. The rare 15cm sIG 33 auf Fahrgestell PzKpfw II (Sf). Initial prototype vehicles were based on the standard Panzer II hull; however, it was soon discovered that the hull needed to be lengthened by 60cm, as well as increased in width by 32cm, to accommodate the gun. All twelve vehicles were shipped to North Africa in 1942, serving with the 707th and 708th sIG Kp (Sf) Heavy Infantry Gun Companies (SP) and seeing a good deal of action, in particular at Gazala. By 1943 all had been lost, but interestingly, one managed to turn up in Egyptian service during the 1948 Arab-Israeli War.

76. A rare photograph of a Sturmgeschütz 7.5cm Kanone Ausf D in service with the Afrika Korps. Three of these vehicles were sent to North Africa with Abt z b v 288, a special unit, in early 1942, and were used during the Gazala fighting and the capture of Tobruk.

77. A 15cm s FH 13/1 (Sf) auf Geschütz-wagen Lorraine Schlepper (f) SdKfz 135/1. This vehicle was one of 94 produced by the Germans on cap-tured French chassis in July 1942, and the type first served with Panzer-artillerie Abteilung of the 21st Panzer Division in North Africa. Note the two-tone paint scheme of DAK yellow and brown stripes.

78. One rule of desert warfare quickly learned by both sides was never to pass up any service-able vehicle. Here, an ex-British Daimler Mk. II Dingo scout car has been repainted in DAK yellow and bears the German serial WH-733543. Not clear in this print is the name 'Wurzel' immediately below the national insignia.

79. Another view of the same Dingo in German service; note the recogni-tion cross at the rear of the vehicle. Both this and the previous photo-graph were taken on 13 April 1942 near Derna, Libya.

77▲

78▲   79▼

▲80

80. A German reconnaissance unit makes use of a Marmon-Herrington Mk. II. The vehicle still has the original South African serial number.

81. The crew of an SdKfz 250/1 Leichter Schützenpanzerwagen receives its orders from a courier.

82. Scanning the horizon for signs of enemy activity. The two vehicles illustrated are both variants of the SdKfz 251 Mittlerer Schützenpanzerwagen: the vehicle in the foreground is an SdKfz 251/3 Mittlerer Kommandopanzerwagen Ausf B; that in the back-

ground is an SdKfz 251/10 Mittlerer Schützenpanzerwagen (3.7cm Pak). The SdKfz 251/10 was issued to platoon leaders to provide direct fire support.

83. The rarely photographed Saurer Beobachtungspanzer SdKfz 254. Produced in Austria as an armoured artillery observation vehicle for motorized units in the field, it utilized a unique wheel/track suspension system which enabled it to be driven on a road like a truck, and across country like a tank. Unfortunately, this system made the vehicle prone to breakdown.

▼81

82▲ 83▼

▲84

84. An SdKfz 7 belonging to a towed artillery unit, in this case one armed with 88mm anti-tank guns. The crew has added a 7.92mm MG34 for anti-aircraft protection.

85. A 7.62cm FK 36(r) auf Panzerjäger Selbstfahrlafette Zugkraft-wagen 5t SdKfz 6 prepares to fire. Nine of these vehicles were produced (this is number 4), and all served with the 605th Panzer-jägerabteilung, seeing extensive action around Gazala in May and June 1942. Note the white air recognition band on the bonnet.

▼85

86▲

87▲

5. Looking in through the access doors of a 'Diana', a 7.62cm FK
6(r) auf Panzerjäger Selbstfahrlafette Zugkraftwagen 5t SdKfz 6.
7. A close-up view of the gun recoil assembly of the same vehicle.
8. Support troops provide covering fire from behind a 7.62cm FK

36(r) auf Panzerjäger Selbstfahrlafette Zugkraftwagen 5t SdKfz 6.
Note that the soldier nearest the camera is unslinging a captured US
Model 1928 Thompson sub-machine gun with drum magazine.

88 ▼

▲89

89. A column of 4×4 Horch s gl Einh PKW command cars grinds to a halt in the middle of the desert. Two of the vehicles are the standard passenger-carrying version, in this case acting as bases for 2cm Flak anti-aircraft guns (one, in the background, is virtually obscured), whilst to the right is a self-propelled anti-aircraft gun mounting a 2cm Flak 38 in its passenger compartment (official designation 2cm Flak 38 (Sf) auf Schwere Geländegängiger Einheits PKW). The vehicles all appear to be in overall panzer grey, with a roughly sprayed application of DAK yellow, and the only marking visible is the DAK palm tree insignia.

90. On guard against enemy air activity, the crew of a 2cm Flak 38 (Sf) auf Schwere Geländegängiger Einheits PKW 4×4 Horch scans the sky. Two variants of this vehicle were built: early models featured drop sides and usually mounted the 2cm Flak 30 anti-aircraft gun; later versions had a 2cm Flak 38. The crew normally numbered seven, and up to 800 rounds of ammunition could be carried.

91. An SdKfz 7 artillery prime mover tows a 15cm s FH 18 howitzer to the front near Gazala, April 1942. When travelling over great distances the gun would usually be transported in sections, but in this case the crew have elected to keep the gun complete in order to bring it into immediate action once they have reached their destination.

92. Another SdKfz 7 prime mover, from the same unit, offering a good view of the 15cm s FH 18 howitzer and limber. The 15cm s FH 18 howitzer was the primary field piece of the German Army at the time and served on all fronts. Note the 'kill' rings on the gun barrel.

▼90

▲93

93. An SdKfz 7 prime mover with 88mm anti-tank gun in tow moves past a Kübelwagen. The Kübelwagen was the German equivalent of the jeep.

94. Members of a DAK anti-tank artillery unit (SdKfz 7 and 88mm gun) pause before setting up their position. The 88mm proved to be the deadliest gun used in the desert, capable of knocking out any Allied armoured vehicle in service at the time.

95. German soldiers prepare an Italian Carro Veloce CV 35 for transportation. The terrain suggests that the setting is the Tunisian hills, so the photo can probably be dated to early 1943. The Germans made use of several different types of Italian equipment throughout the war, primarily in police and security detachments; it

is known, for example, that the 'Hermann Göring' division used a number of ex-Italian armoured vehicles during the fighting in Tunisia. The paint scheme appears to be the overall dark desert brown colour favoured by the Italians, with a random pattern of green on top. The vehicle retains the original Italian markings, in this case three vertical white stripes on a red block, indicating a vehicle of the 3rd Platoon, 1st Company.

96. A captured Daimler Mk. II Dingo scout car passes an SdKfz 250/3 Leichter Funkpanzerwagen. The markings on the rear of the SdKfz 250/3 indicate that the two vehicles belonged to the 21st Panzer Division as part of a towed artillery battery. The photograph was taken some time after the division moved into Tunisia in 1943.

▼94

97. Mud and dust proved to be the greatest enemy of machinery during the North African campaign. Here a member of the DAK washes down the wheel of a captured Daimler Mk. II 'Dingo' scout car.

98. A PzKpfw II Ausf F in Tunisia, 1943. The Ausf F was the last model in the standard Panzer II series, and was introduced in March 1941. The vehicle mounted a 2cm Kwk 30 L/55 gun, and served as a light reconnaissance vehicle. This example is from an unidentified unit, possibly the 15th Panzer Division; the turret number 'II 05' indicates a vehicle of the commander of the 2nd Battalion, 5th Company. Note the numerous 'jerry cans', which could carry either water or fuel.

99. The same PzKpfw II Ausf F in the Tunisian hills.

100. A PzKpfw III Ausf J in the Tunisian hills. The unit is not certain, but the 15th Panzer Division is known to have applied only company numbers to its tanks in Africa. In this case the number is a red '5', indicating a vehicle of the 5th Company. The photograph was taken during the Tunisian fighting in 1943.

▲97 ▼98

▲101 ▼102

101. A PzKpfw III Ausf L of an unidentified unit in Tunisia, 1943. Distinguishing features of the Ausf L included an increase from 30mm to 57mm in armour thickness on the turret front, an additional 20mm of armour on the hull front and the long-barrel 5cm Kwk 39 L/60 tank gun. On this particular vehicle, the crew has taken the precaution of stowing sandbags and track links.

102. A PzKpfw III Ausf N of either the 10th or the 21st Panzer Division, Tunisia, 1943. The Ausf N was the last gun-armed version in the series, and was introduced in late 1942. Armed with the 7.5cm Kwk L/24 gun, the vehicle usually served in heavy tank companies.

103. A PzKpfw III Ausf J on the move in Tunisia, 1943. The vehicle illustrated is a late version of the type and has additional 20mm spaced armour fitted to the superstructure front giving a total thickness of 50mm. A good deal of personal gear is stowed externally, to give more space inside the vehicle, whilst brush has been added to break up the outline shape.

▲104 ▼105

106▲ 107▼

104. A close-up of the turret of a PzKpfw III Ausf N in Tunisia, early 1943.
105. PzKpfw IV Ausf Gs of either the 10th or the 21st Panzer Division move through the Tunisian foothills, 1943. The Panzer IV Ausf G mounted the 7.5cm Kwk 40 L/48 tank gun, and was capable of knocking out any Allied vehicle fielded in the desert at that time. Note the many white-striped cans for carrying water – unmarked cans were reserved for fuel.
106. Another PzKpfw IV Ausf G of the same unit.
107. One final PzKpfw IV in the same column. One member of the crew has taken the trouble to mark out the profile of a girl in the dust on the right mud guard.

▲108

▲109

108. A PzKpfw VI Ausf E (Tiger 1) of Schwerer Panzer Abteilungen (Heavy Tank Company) 501 in Tunisia, 1943. No markings other than the turret number, in this case '732', can be seen; this number indicates a vehicle of Panzer Regiment 7, which was attached to the 10th Panzer Division after February 1943. The unit took part in the savage fighting in Tunisia and was virtually wiped out.

109. Feldmarschal Rommel strolls past a column of knocked-out US M3 Gun Motor Carriages destroyed during the Battle of Kasserine Pass in February 1943.

110. Rommel passes a knocked-out British Crusader Mk. II CS (close-support) tank somewhere in the Tunisian hills, 1943.

111. Large quantities of American equipment were captured after the Battle of Kasserine Pass; here, Rommel draws abreast an ex-US M3 halftrack. At the rear of the column is an SdKfz 251 Ausf C Mittlerer Schützenpanzerwagen, the standard APC of the German Army at the time. Other photographs in this series indicate that these vehicles belong to the 10th Panzer Division.

▲112　▼113

112. An SdKfz 263 Panzerfunkwagen 8-Rad passes the same M3 halftrack. The SdKfz 263 appears to be in overall desert brown with a rough application of mud applied over that. The M3 retains its US scheme of overall olive drab discoloured by dust; in addition, a white German cross has been applied to the bonnet. It has been estimated that, by this time, over two-thirds of the vehicles in service with the DAK were of either US or British origin.
113. A Sturmgeschütz 40 Ausf F SdKfz 142/1 in the Tunisian hills, 1943. This vehicle belonged to the 'Hermann Göring' Panzer Division, and was painted overall dark yellow. While not apparent

in this photograph, the only marking carried other than the German Balkenkreuz was a section letter in black, on the rear hull.
114. A column of ex-US vehicles in DAK service, including three M3 halftracks, a jeep and a GMC 2½-ton truck; the halftracks are towing US M3A1 37mm anti-tank guns. All the vehicles retain their original overall olive drab paint scheme, with US serial numbers, but have received random applications of mud to break up the dark finish.
115. Another view of the same column on the move, showing a GMC 2½-ton truck, three jeeps and at least five M3 halftracks.

▲116

116. British personnel examine a captured PzKpfw VI Ausf E Tiger 1 tank in the Kounine Hills of Tunisia. The photograph was taken in April 1943, by which time the DAK had become ineffective as a fighting force. In early March Rommel had been recalled to Berlin, where he requested the evacuation of his remaining troops from Tunisia, an appeal which resulted in his being replaced by von Arnim, who commanded the German forces until they surrendered in May of 1943. The vehicle illustrated belonged to the 3rd Platoon of s Pz Abt 501, which was all but destroyed during the final fighting in Tunisia. No markings are visible except for part of the

white-outlined, red turret number. Note the 'kill' rings on the gun barrel, an indication of how deadly the Tiger could be in combat.
117. A final view of an abandoned PzKpfw IV Ausf E Tiger 1 tank of s Pz Abt 501 in the Tunisian hills, April 1943. No markings are visible, but the vehicle appears to be finished in the overall olive green scheme adopted by some tanks for the fighting in Tunisia. This vehicle bears mute testimony to the final collapse of the DAK in North Africa; the Tiger was the deadliest German tank of the war, but only small numbers reached those troops that needed them most.

▼117